Self-Love Coloring Book & Journal

Heart Art for Loving Yourself More Everyday

I NEVER serve from my reserves

I am worth taking good care of

feed the feminine first

I am nourished

i am supported

I am cared for

i am well rested

fill me up

Retain

sustain

I Receive all that i need

Written & Illustrated by
Christine Arylo

The Path of Self-Love ™:
An international self-love school & movement

Previous Bestselling Self-Love Books
by Christine Arylo

Choosing ME Before WE

Madly in Love with ME

Reform Your Inner Mean Girl

☾ ☾ ☾ ☾ ☽

Meditation CD

Madly in Love with ME – Self-Love Meditations for the Heart + Soul
With music & mantra by Karen Drucker

☾ ☾ ☾ ☾ ☽

The Path of Self-Love School –
Programs, Retreats, Classes, & Teacher Trainings

Visit www.PathofSelfLove.org

Published by The Path of Self-Love
Valley of the Moon, Sonoma, California
©2017 Christine Arylo

ISBN # 978-0-692-90181-6

Welcome!

HELLO AND WELCOME TO THE SELF-LOVE COLORING BOOK & JOURNAL! Inside this book you will find both illustrations (known as "Heart Art") and inquiries for connecting and communicating more deeply with your heart and soul. As I made each image and wrote each word, I did so with the intention that as you journey through the pages of this coloring book, the power of love, courage, compassion, and confidence will come streaming through you. Using the combination of image, color, mantras, and inquiries, consider this an invitation to express yourself, empower yourself, trust yourself, be compassionate with yourself, and make loving choices for yourself.

Self-love is one of those things that sounds like a good idea, but sometimes can feel a little selfish. But loving yourself is not something you do instead of loving others. Love is a both/and equation: The more loved, cared for, supported, and strong you feel inside, the more capacity you have to love, care, support, and give encouragement to others.

SELF-LOVE IS SIMPLY LOVE DIRECTED TOWARDS THE SELF. THE SAME KIND OF LOVE YOU GIVE TO ANOTHER PERSON – COMPASSION, CARE, COURAGE, ACCEPTANCE, ACKNOWLEDGEMENT, CELEBRATION – YOU GIVE TO YOURSELF.

The way I teach self-love, which I have been doing for over a decade, is practical, powerful and fun. Sometimes self-love can feel so vast, esoteric or vague that you don't know where to start, what you need or if you are really loving yourself well at all. At The Path of Self-Love School, we teach people how to strengthen all 11 types of self-love – from self-care to self-empowerment to self-worth – which together create the strong foundation of inner confidence, compassion and courage we all need to thrive.

I chose to create this coloring journal because I desired to design an experience that could open you up and give you enhanced access to that beautiful, strong, tender heart of yours. A place to come to in order to conjure up feelings of love and courage on days when you are feeling down, alone or scared. A way to turn off the outside chatter and tune into your heart and soul when you can use a boost of clarity, confidence or inner truth. A practice for being in conversation and communion with your Self – your heart's desires, your soul's truth, YOU.

IMAGE, COLOR, SYMBOL, WORDS, AND INQUIRY ALL HAVE THE POWER TO TAKE YOU BEYOND YOUR MENTAL MIND INTO DEEPER PLACES WITHIN WHERE THE GUIDANCE YOU SEEK, THE LOVE AND COMPASSION YOU NEED, AND THE COURAGE YOU DESIRE ALL LIVE. REMEMBER, EVERYTHING YOU SEEK ON THE OUTSIDE IS ALREADY WITHIN YOU ON THE INSIDE.

In a world in which so much attention is placed on the external, by making the personal choice to choose the loving action towards yourself every day in every way, you will love others better, and you will be part of creating a more peaceful, prosperous world where all people are treated and held as sacred, including you.

With Great Heart,

Christine Arylo
Founder of The Path of Self-Love School

How to Use the Self-Love Coloring Book & Journal

How It's Organized

♡ The Self-Love Tree and the 10 Branches of Self-Love

I WANT TO MAKE SURE YOU RECEIVE A TASTE OF ALL THE PARTS OF SELF-LOVE THAT MAKE UP A STRONG INNER FOUNDATION. After many years of research and working with over 35,000 people around the world, we have identified 10 specific types of self-love that are both related and distinct. We call these "the branches of self-love." Think of self-love like a tree. Just like a tree, you want all the branches and the roots to be strong so the entire tree is healthy and strong. Most people have a few weak branches and a few strong branches. The branches of self-love are:

- **SELF-AWARENESS & HONESTY**
- **SELF-ACCEPTANCE**
- **SELF-CARE**
- **SELF-COMPASSION & FORGIVENESS**
- **SELF-EMPOWERMENT**
- **SELF-ESTEEM**
- **SELF-EXPRESSION**
- **SELF-RESPECT & HONOR**
- **SELF-TRUST**
- **SELF-PLEASURE**

The roots of self-love are self-worth. Through this journal, you'll experience all 10 branches and the roots of self-worth.

For each branch of self-love, you will find:

1. **The Definition** – gives you context for the specific kind of self-love you're working with
2. **Signs of Self-Love Strength** – so you can check in to see where you're weak & strong
3. **Two Heart Art Illustrations** – for you to color and connect with your heart
4. **Heart & Soul Sparks** – inquiries to make the Heart Art even more personal

♡ Heart Art

HEART ART IS A SPECIFIC KIND OF ART THAT IS INTENTIONALLY CREATED TO HEAL, FREE AND COMMUNICATE WITH THE HEART. It is a technique we use at The Path of Self-Love School to get us out of our heads and into our hearts, where we can access deeper levels of wisdom, truth, joy and love. When done intentionally, it has the power to transform the 'stuff' inside your heart that can weigh you down, distract you or drive you to make self-sabotaging choices. Fear. Shame. Blame. Anger. Doubt. All that shadowy stuff that we don't necessarily want to talk about, but that if we don't move out of our hearts, gets stuck and causes us to settle, sacrifice and sabotage ourselves.

Heart Art combines the power of image, symbol, color, and words to invoke and pour the most powerful "medicine" we have to heal and free our hearts: **LOVE.**

Every illustration was intentionally hand-drawn by me to invoke the specific type of self-love you'll be working with as you color.

The process of coloring + journaling can soothe the tender places within you, empower the courageous places, and expand the places desiring to be more expressed. Also, because you have created this piece of art with intention from your heart, when you complete the piece, you can use it as "self-love super power!" Put it somewhere you can see it and it can reflect back to you what your heart needs to feel and hear to keep making the most loving, supportive and empowering choices for yourself.

Heart Art by Love Ambassador Gretchen Bladek, Love Jeans

You'll find two pieces of Heart Art for each of the types of self-love.

1. The Feminine Heart - Female images, each with a prominent spiral heart, along with specific words and symbols for that self-love branch. My intention is that you make this image your own by the colors and markings you choose for her face, hair and body. I often color her hair magenta and gold and have colored her skin everything from magenta to gold to brown to pink (I am slightly obsessed with the colors magenta and gold)! I did my best to create an image that could relate to as many women and girls as possible. Considering we are all so different in face but so similar in heart, I realize that task was perhaps impossible. And for this, I ask for grace and give you full permission to make her yours.

True Story: This female image emerged after three years of me actively "looking for her." Sketching, doodling, and finally, a pilgrimage to Paris with the very specific intention to "find my art" and a dream realized of living in Italy for a summer. It all came together after seeing two things. One, the spiraled heart appeared over and over again in the strong and beautiful iron gates and doors all over Paris and Italy – a symbol to me of the strength of the feminine heart. Two, "graffiti" on the side of a building on a Parisian side street of a woman with the hair I had been searching for how to draw! I snapped a photo, went straight back to the flat we were staying at and drew the first piece of Heart Art, "I am Sacred."

2. The Love Mantra Mirror - Love Mantras are powerful statements that generate the vibration of love in your body and mind and have "super power" to transform the fearful, sabotaging voice of what I call your "Inner Mean Girl" into the loving truth of your Inner Wisdom. The Love Mantras were created to be like mirrors you can look into to reflect back to you the loving, supportive, and empowering truth. Each Love Mantra – which are real mantras the students at The Path of Self-Love School and I have created and used – is set within a frame with symbols and shapes specific to that self-love branch.

Why do mantras work? It's not voodoo; it's just simple science with a dash of spirituality. When words come out of your mouth, they create sound. Sound is vibration. Unlike affirmations – which work mostly on the mental plane and can feel like you are trying to convince yourself of something – Love Mantras work on a vibrational level to shift your inner feelings and emotions (inside your body, mind, and spirit) into a vibration of love. The word mantra means "a sacred message, charm or counsel." Love Mantras are sacred messages that counsel you to listen to and feel love instead of fear, shame and blame. They are like self-love prayers or self-love stands. Making the mantra visual makes it go through your brain differently. So seeing this reflection on a consistent basis, changes the way you see yourself and your reality.

♡ Heart & Soul Sparks

HOW DO YOU COMMUNICATE WITH YOUR HEART AND SOUL TO FIND OUT WHAT IS REALLY GOING ON INSIDE OF YOU? IN ADDITION TO IMAGE AND COLOR, YOU CAN USE THE SUPER POWER TOOL OF "INQUIRY." You ask yourself powerful questions with the intention of finding deeper wisdom and illuminating new insight – not seeking definitive answers. Our brains want specific, finite and secure answers to feel safe. Our hearts, however, know that the world works in much subtler ways, and that great lives are lived from the heart, not the head. Great lives are lived from compassion and courage (which come from the heart) and the clarity and confidence to follow one's soul path and Inner Wisdom regardless of what conventional wisdom says or what everyone else is doing.

I've given you a few simple but mighty inquiries for each branch of self-love to spark your heart and soul into deeper levels of wisdom and expanded levels of insight. Use these inquiries as journaling prompts to learn more about what's going on inside of you and what messages your heart and soul may have for you. Take the wisdom and insight you gather and add that to the Heart Art to make it even more personal.

Tips for Super Powering Your Heart Art

Heart Art can be a powerful way to deepen your personal practice + your relationship with yourself. Just like any relationship, the more time you spend together and the more care you give it, the stronger it becomes. The same is true about your relationship with yourself. You will better know what you need, be more attuned with your truth, and feel more confident about who you are and the direction your life is headed if you connect with your heart more often.

Making Heart Art is like taking "self-love medicine." It can calm and soothe your heart, ignite your passion, make you feel powerful and courageous, and help you tap into your Inner Wisdom and truth. At The Path of Self-Love School, we teach that self-love is a practice, a choice and a path that you get to participate in every day for the rest of your life.

I invite you to use this book as a practice to deepen your connection to yourself – you are worth it! Here are some ideas:

1. Choose a specific type of self-love and proactively strengthen it or give yourself a "Love Boost" on the days you are feeling down - ask your heart what kind of love it needs to receive, open the book to a random page and color and journal with that.

2. Take a Self-Love Assessment at www.selfloveassessment.com to see which branches are weakest and strongest - this is a 100-question assessment that has been tested to measure the strength of the ten branches of self-love.

3. Choose to strengthen one branch per week or month - do the journaling and coloring on the same day each week; the consistency will help you stay committed. Or do one branch a month. Or use the moon phases to create sacred space on the new and full moon (I this call mooni-festing and it definitely gives you super power.)

4. Use the inquiries to connect and communicate with your heart and soul - you don't always have to color, you can just pick up the book and journal.

5. Add personalized words and images to make the Heart Art even more your own - go back to images you have started coloring and add words and images you need to see and hear now.

♡ Color & Journal with Intention

This Heart Art book is no ordinary coloring book. It's been created with intention to give you the super power to communicate with your heart and soul, to nourish and empower them and yourself with the specific kind of love you need to feel strong, safe, seen, connected, clear and confident. So when you color and journal, do it as an act of love for yourself, feeling your inner power to create and cultivate what you need.

As you color and journal, create this Heart Art just as if you were creating it as a gift for someone you love. If you are working with a specific branch of self-love, read the definition and consider the ways you are strong and weak in that area using the signs of a strong self-love. Then as you color and journal, imagine giving and receiving that specific kind of self-love medicine.

Keep the Journal with You

KEEP THE JOURNAL SOMEWHERE YOU CAN SEE IT – next to your bed, on your desk, near the sacred space you have in your home just for you (if you don't have a personal sacred space, make one). Keep the book in your purse or bag and use it as a break during your workday or in waiting rooms or on the plane. Take it to dinner with you (dates with yourself!). Take it on vacation or make a stay-cation for an evening or a whole day that is just about you expressing your creative self. I carry markers in my purse for this purpose – spontaneous Heart Art rocks!

Bring on the Color + Play!

If you haven't been to the art store lately, it's time to pick up some colorful supplies and let yourself PLAY – a set of colored pencils, crayons or my personal favorite, markers. If you don't have color in your life, you can't expect to live a vibrant life. I love using markers for that specific reason: vibrancy. That means they will also bleed through the pages, but not to worry! Even if you do color through to your writing, think of it like alchemy! The words and the images and the color are blending together. Different markers have different levels of bleed-through, so experiment and see what you like.

When choosing colors, I recommend choosing one color to start with and then pausing to take in what you have done so far. Then choose another color and add that into the spaces that seem to be 'calling for' it. I like to let the Heart Art show me what it wants to be vs. stressing myself out about what color should go where. It's like letting your Inner Wisdom do the coloring – throughout the process, pause, breathe and feel what you are creating. Let your heart show you the way. I also like to add flair to my Heart Art.

HERE ARE A FEW IDEAS:

1. **Add 'dots'** inside the shapes or around letters.
2. **Add markings, symbols or words** on the feminine images or around or inside the mirror mantra frames – including her face and hair.
3. **Make patterns with swirls or lines** inside the bigger spaces.

Give Your Inner Wisdom the Microphone When Journaling

*Heart Art by Love Ambassador
Katherine Torrini*

Use the lined and the blank pages provided for journaling the Heart + Soul Sparks. If you are reading the Madly in Love with ME book, which goes into depth on each of the 10 branches of self-love, use this journal with the Daring Adventures of Love and ME Moments in the book and add what you reveal into your Heart Art.

Journaling is a powerful way to connect with your heart and illuminate insights not otherwise seen. You don't have to be a professional writer to journal – if a 7-year-old can keep a diary, you can write and journal! There are many creative writing practices; here are two suggestions:

1. Read the Heart and Soul Sparks. Then before writing, connect with your Inner Wisdom so it is the one responding – it's as simple as closing your eyes, putting your hand on your heart, and taking a deep breath. This activates the parasympathetic nervous system in your body + tunes you into the rhythm and beat of your heart.

2. Use the blank journal page with no lines as well as the ones with lines – no-lined writing frees you up. Dare to write outside the lines!

On a technical note: When you choose your writing device, test it to see how it appears on the other side of the page. Markers like Crayola Super Tips or Pentel Points tend not to bleed through to the other side; so if you like to write in color, as I do, use those. You can also use pencil or pen. Sharpies and other alcohol-based markers like Copic and Prismacolor will bleed through, so I save them for the coloring, not the writing.

Share the Love with Others You Love

Heart Art can be done with yourself, and you can also super power the love by making Heart Art with others – family, friends, kids, a girls' night in, a woman's circle, your book club. You can share one book with the group or get multiple books. You could all focus on the same branch of self-love or allow each person to choose the branch they desire to grow. Then:

1. Have each person share the branch of self-love they chose and why
2. Journal and color one piece of Heart Art each
3. Come back together and share what you learned
4. Share the Heart Art and share what you see in each other's images.

You can make the gathering light and informal – music, snacks and vino or Pellegrino. You can take it deeper and guide the group through one of the branches of self-love and dialogue about it collectively and individually.

At The Path of Self-Love School, each year for the international Self-Love Day on February 13th, we create a special Self-Love Circle guidebook + training session for Love Ambassadors who desire to bring women or girls together for an afternoon or evening. If you'd like to receive that, go to http://www.selfloveambassador.com/.

Make Your Heart Art Visible in a Place Where It Can Keep Working on You

You can keep the images and journaling in this book all in one place and use the book for a love boost when you need it. Or you can take the pages out and put them where you can see them and they can inspire you. Tape them to your mirror, paste them inside your yearly journal cover, or put them on your desk or your bedside table. Heart Art loves to be seen! You can snap a photo and make it a screensaver, a wallpaper for your phone or a post on social media with your writing. If you share your images, please credit the Self-Love Coloring Journal from Christine Arylo and The Path of Self-Love School.

If you choose to take the image out of the book, slowly tear it out of the book – mindfully. It will come out of the book with the edges rough. You can keep the rough-edged look or you can cut with scissors around the frame. Whichever option you choose, don't try to be a perfectionist about it. Part of self-love is loving all parts just as they are – even those that don't look "perfect."

 ## Learn to Create Your Own Heart Art

These images are based on The Path of Self-Love technology – processes, methods, assessments, meditations, inquiries – I created over a decade of testing, experimenting with and teaching self-love. We teach both individuals who desire to strengthen their self-love for themselves and those who desire to teach or share it with others. Find out more about the teacher training for leading groups and circles, using the self-love technology to enhance your work, or deepening your own self-love journey and making Heart Art for yourself at The Path of Self-Love School website.

Self-Awareness & Self-Honesty

A deep understanding of who you are and who you are not, with an unwavering commitment to truth about how your actions, thoughts and choices affect your reality and the people and world around you.

Signs of Strong Self-Awareness & Self-Honesty:

On a scale of 1 to 5, with 5 being always true, 3 sometimes true and 1 not true, rank your self-love strength "I..."

- Know who I am and who I am not.

- Know how I differ from the environments I grew up in, live in and work in.

- Am honest with myself in all aspects of my life, even when it's hard.

- Embrace who I have been and who I am today.

- Am curious about & actively exploring who I am becoming and evolving into.

Heart & Soul Sparks

add personal spark to your heart art

- 3 words that describe you

- 3 words that don't describe you + their opposite

- 3 words that describe who you would love to grow into

Write these words that reflect who you are in a way that reflects the energy of what you are describing. For example, if one of your words is "courageous," then write it with bold letters and color it with bold colors like red, green or orange. If "calm" is word you are growing into, write the letters in a softer manner. Heart Art Bonus: Include symbols that go with the words that are meaningful for you. For example, with courage include a heart. With calm, include water waves.

Self-Acceptance

Embracing and loving all parts of yourself - who you are, as you are, body, personality, past and present without regret, shame or judgment, offering yourself the same unconditional love as a mother offers her child.

Signs of Strong Self-Acceptance:

On a scale of 1 to 5, with 5 being always true, 3 sometimes true and 1 not true, rank your self-love strength "I..."

- Love being me. I don't wish to or try to be someone else.

- Love all of me, even the parts that are hard to love.

- Rarely compare myself to others, to external standards or to who I think I should be or used to be.

- Accept my body for who she is, now. I don't talk bad about my body. I transform body hate into body love.

- Focus my energy on changing and growing what I can and surrendering what I cannot change.

Heart & Soul Sparks

add personal spark to your heart art

- What one part of my body would I love to love more?

- What one part of my personality – quality, trait – would I love to embrace more?

- What one part about who I have been in the past – but may have hidden away – would I love to invite back?

Write the body part, personality part, and part of who you have been in your past on the three hearts at the bottom of the Mantra Mirror. On your Feminine Heart Art, make your self-love active by choosing to love these parts of yourself back by writing self-love promise statements:

I promise to love my <insert body part.>
I promise to embrace that I <insert personality part.>
I promise to reclaim <insert the part of you from your past you have hidden
& are bringing back.>

Self-Compassion & Self-Forgiveness

இ இ இ இ இ

The choice to open your heart and offer yourself kindness, gentleness, forgiveness, understanding, and patience – whenever you need it without cause or condition or judgment.

Signs of Strong Self-Compassion

On a scale of 1 to 5, with 5 being always true, 3 sometimes true and 1 not true, rank your self-love strength "I..."

- Support myself when I falter or fail.

- Forgive myself for the big and little things.

- Engage in more compassionate, supportive self-love talk than critical and negative self-talk.

- Tell myself when I struggle or fail: "I am doing my best, I am learning and stretching and that's okay!"

- Am patient, gentle and understanding with myself just like I would be with a child who is learning to walk. Instead of pressuring myself when I am stretching, struggling or trying something new, I apply patience.

Heart & Soul Sparks

add personal spark to your heart art

Think of an area in your life that you are struggling in or feeling stretched, stressed or unsupported in. Channel the compassionate words your heart needs to hear and feel by closing your eyes, putting your hand on your heart, taking a deep breath and asking these questions one by one. Write down whatever first comes and add the words to your Heart Art.

- What are the words I need to hear right now to soothe my heart?

- If my best friend or child was in this situation what would I say to them?

- What is the loving truth?

Self-Care

Choosing to make sure that you get what you need on all levels –
physically, spiritually, emotionally, and mentally – every day.

Signs of Strong Self Care:

On a scale of 1 to 5, with 5 being always true, 3 sometimes true and 1 not true, rank your self-love strength "I…"

◎ Feel replenished, nourished and fulfilled. My body and mind get good food and sleep.

◎ Feel supported and well taken care of. I have what I need to take care of myself.

◎ Feel full of energy, vibrant and alive – physically and emotionally. I am healthy.

◎ Take breaks to replenish, rest, and recharge consistently. I can relax without feeling guilty.

◎ Have a balanced life in which all areas – career, home, relationships, health, wealth, & spirit– are well cared for.

Heart & Soul Sparks

add personal spark to your heart art

Most people know how to take care of themselves. The struggle is: 1. Giving yourself the *permission* to take the self-caring act no matter what, 2. Knowing and being able to articulate what you actually need, 3. Giving too much and not receiving enough so you drain your life force and resources, 4. Putting others needs above your own instead of making it a both/and equation. Journal on these inquiries and take a stand for yourself to get what you need, even if that means disappointing another. To tap into your inner wisdom on this, it can help to read the inquiry, then close your eyes, take a breath, put your hand on your heart and then ask for inner guidance.

 What do I need to receive today?

 In what ways – to whom or to what - am I over giving my time, energy, money, attention, care?

 What do I need to say NO to in order to re-balance what I give and what I receive?

 What do I need to say YES to in order to take care of myself?

Heart Art Bonus: Add this self-love promise to your Heart Art:

"I promise to take care of myself, even if that means disappointing another."

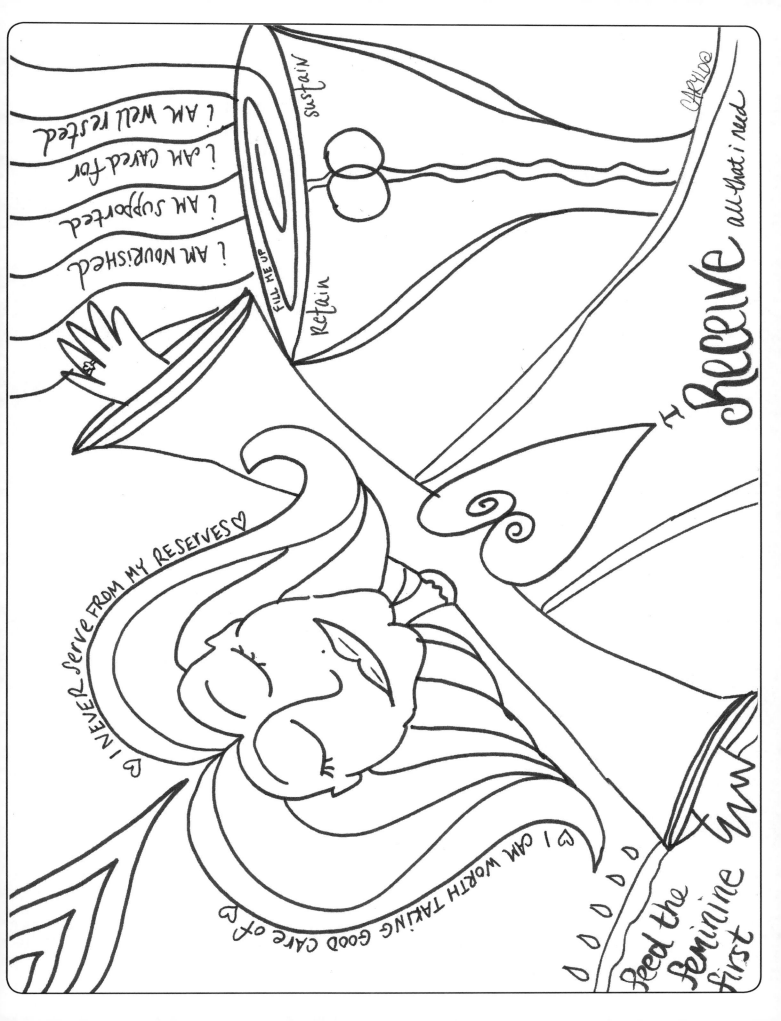

Self-Esteem

A strong belief in and regard for yourself. A strong confidence in your ability to do and be anything. An inner belief that you are gifted, you have gifts and your gifts are valuable.

Signs of Strong Self-Esteem:

On a scale of 1 to 5, with 5 being always true, 3 sometimes true and 1 not true, rank your self-love strength "I..."

- Believe I can do and be anything and I go for it.

- Have a high level of self-confidence and self-regard. It takes a lot to shake my inner belief.

- Stand up for my beliefs and ideas without apology even if others don't agree.

- Am proud of what I accomplish and receive acknowledgement easily.

- Strive to be the best me I can be. I value my gifts, efforts and talents.

Heart & Soul Sparks

add personal spark to your heart art

One of the biggest differences between people with a strong self-esteem – an inner confidence and value of oneself that is solid – is how they see, hold and value their innate gifts. People with strong self-esteem believe they are talented, special, wise and gifted, and use that inner confidence to support others to shine and share their gifts too. Bring your unique gifts out to shine by journaling on these heart inquiries to reveal some of your gifts and then write them on the Heart Art with the intention to claim and value them at a deeper level from within.

- I am really good at... _listening, empathy, compassionate_
- When I was little, I just loved... _drawing, coloring, crafts_
- I feel happiest and most alive when... _I'm in contact c my inner wisdom, love_
- People always tell me that... _I'm competent_
- When I am really in my zone of brilliance, I notice that people around me... _listen_
- You can always count on me to... _do what I say_
- I know that I am gifted at... _being present, watching movement correcting movement_

34

Self-Empowerment

Choosing to take charge of and responsibility for your life by acting to create the life you really desire, without apology or requiring approval from others.

Signs of Strong Self-Empowerment:

On a scale of 1 to 5, with 5 being always true, 3 sometimes true and 1 not true, rank your self-love strength "I…"

- Take responsibility for my life circumstances. I am not a victim or martyr.

- Change what I don't like about my life.

- Go for my dreams. I know what I desire and I am actively making my dreams a reality.

- Feel strong and act courageously. I take risks to go for what I desire, even when I feel afraid.

- Choose to live my life on my terms and according to my truth and conscience even if that means upsetting another.

Heart & Soul Sparks

add personal spark to your heart art

When you have strong self-empowerment you source your power from the inside. You don't give your power away or look to others to give you permission, authority or the answers. You are 'sovereign' – you hold the reins of your life and you reign over your life like a Queen or King. A self-empowered person knows how to transform self-doubt or fear so they can step powerfully into their lives to make shift happen. Think of an area of your life that you desire to shift or that you feel unsure, scared or doubtful in, and use these inquiries to tap into your personal power line:

- What circumstances would I like to be different from what I am experiencing now?

- Remembering a time you took a courageous action – tell the story and write 3 words that describe what you felt like inside.

- If I was acting as the Queen or King of my life, and believed I had the power to make shift happen, what 3 next steps would I take?

Heart Art Bonus: Make a personalized power mantra that supports you to take the reins of your life and step forward, courageously, into the uncertainty with a full and wide-open heart.

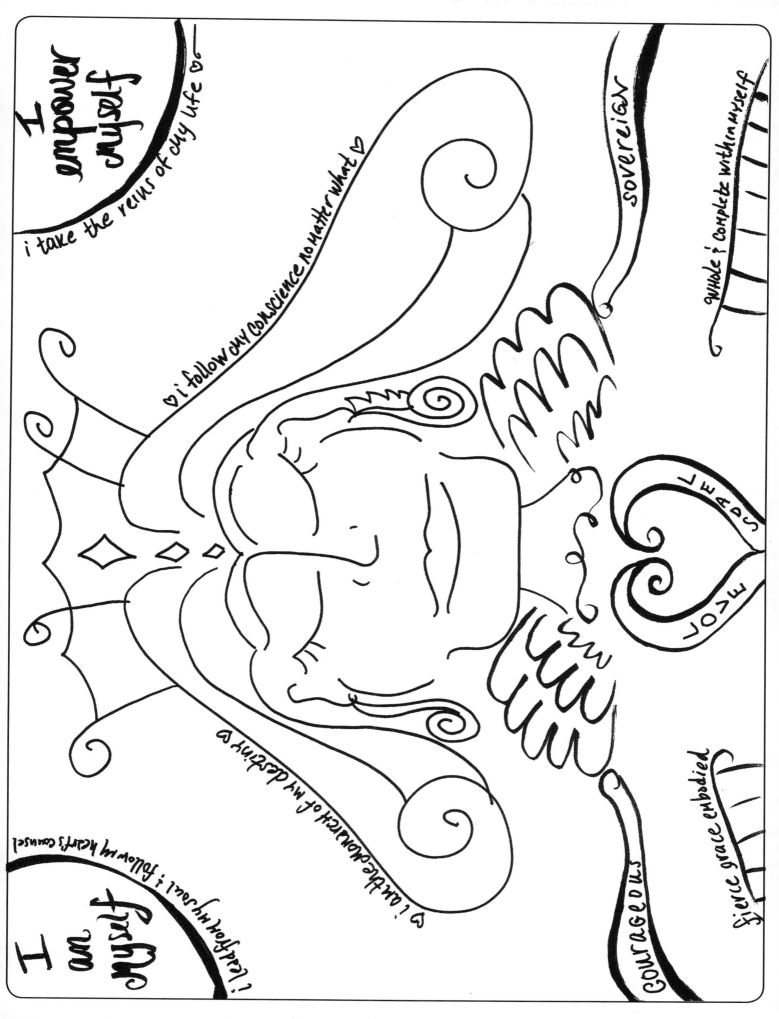

Self-Expression

Choosing to let the world see you, fully, truthfully, and without apology or holding back. Full, free expression of your heart and soul.

Signs of Strong Self-Expression:

On a scale of 1 to 5, with 5 being always true, 3 sometimes true and 1 not true, rank your self-love strength "I..."

- ⊚ Openly express myself in all parts of my life. I am myself whether at work or with friends and family. I don't hold back or hide parts of myself.

- ⊚ Express my thoughts, feelings and gifts fully and freely, even when it makes others uncomfortable.

- ⊚ Feel seen for who I really am.

- ⊚ Bring my unique flair to everything I do. I am myself. I have no challenge doing things differently from others. I don't need to blend in.

- ⊚ Feel like I am living full out, in full color, truly living a life that reflects who I am.

Heart & Soul Sparks

add personal spark to your heart art

Many people don't feel seen or fully expressed because they don't see themselves or are afraid to fully let themselves be seen. There are parts that are repressed on the inside, dying to be free to express through to the outside. One way to find these repressed parts is to notice what you admire in others. What you see in others that inspires you, makes you feel alive, or even jealous is also inside of you, although how it expresses differs. Your inner "essence" recognizes their "essence" as kindred. Reveal more of your essence by choosing a shero or hero in the 5 categories below. Write their name + a list of qualities you admire about them. Then circle the qualites that resonate most and add them to your Heart Art as an intentional act to express this essence more.

- ♡ Your Field of Work
- ♡ Fictional Character
- ♡ World Leader – Spiritual/Political/Social
- ♡ TV/Film
- ♡ History

Self-Pleasure

*Choosing to consistently create, receive, and experience joy,
ensuring that your soul is fully fed and nourished.*

Signs of Strong Self-Pleasure:

On a scale of 1 to 5, with 5 being always true, 3 sometimes true and 1 not true, rank your self-love strength "I…"

- Feel happy more than unhappy. Even in moments of stress I can find a place of joy within me.

- Have a healthy balance of work and play. I do things that bring me joy daily, even if they aren't 'productive.'

- Feel joy-full and fulfilled. I am fulfilled on all levels – emotionally, mentally, spiritually and physically.

- Savor life. I stop often to smell the roses and enjoy life, no matter how busy I am or how much work there is to do.

- Know when I need more play and pleasure, and I know what to do to have fun and generate joy.

Heart & Soul Sparks

add personal spark to your heart art

Joy is food for your soul. If you don't get enough on a regular basis your soul will shrivel up and starve and you will be cranky, crabby, overwhelmed, depressed and drained. As we become adults, we forget what brings us joy, we prioritize productivity over play and pleasure and we suffer. Part of the path of self-love is diving deep into your heart to remember what brings you joy and then taking a stand to make sure your soul stays nourished. Journal on these inquiries to reveal what generates joy for you. Add these to your Heart Art and in the times when you feel depleted, discouraged, or not the beautiful centered presence you are, use these to generate JOY pronto.

I am happiest when…
I feel most alive when…
I feel more free when…
When I was a little, I loved to…
My soul gets nourished when…
I feel most cared for when…
I just love…

Self-Respect and Self-Honor

✺✺✺✺✺

The unwavering commitment to make only choices that respect and honor the sacred soul that you are.

Signs of Strong Self-Respect & Self-Honor:

On a scale of 1 to 5, with 5 being always true, 3 sometimes true and 1 not true, rank your self-love strength "I..."

- Respect all parts of me – my spirit, mind, body and feelings. I don't discount, disregard or degrade my body, intelligence, feelings or experience.

- Only have loving, respectful relationships – family, friends, work, romantic. I expect all people to be good to me, and they are or I don't have relationships with them.

- Respect others, but not in lieu of respecting myself.

- Share my body and spirit only with those who honor its sacredness. I treat my body as a temple.

- Stand up for myself. If I am in a situation that is not honoring me, I speak up.

Heart & Soul Sparks

add personal spark to your heart art

If you truly believed you – your body, mind, spirit and feelings - were SACRED, what would you change about the relationships and situations in your life? To honor and respect yourself is to hold yourself as sacred, just as you would anything or anyone that was precious to you. Tapping into the self-love branch of self-honesty for help, illuminate where in your life you are currently settling for less that what holds you as the sacred being you are.

- What situations and relationships are currently not honoring your feelings? Your body? Your spirit? If these parts were honored, what would that look like?

- In what parts of your life are you settling for less than your heart and soul desire? What does your heart and soul desire?

- What relationships are not respectful and honoring of you? Why do you keep them? And what do you desire instead?

Then take a self-love stand by personalizing your Heart Art by adding your name and/ or your heart and soul desires with the intention of holding and honoring yourself and your desires as sacred.

LOVE YOU

IT IS GOOD TO ASK FOR WHAT I DESIRE

I Promise

I WILL

Never Settle

for Less Than

MY

HEART & SOUL

DESIRE

I CHOOSE MYSELF, WITH LOVE

I DESERVE MY DESIRES

Self-Trust

Choosing to listen to and follow the guidance of your inner guidance, believing you know what is right for you, even when other people think or say otherwise.

Signs of Strong Self-Trust:

On a scale of 1 to 5, with 5 being always true, 3 sometimes true and 1 not true, rank your self-love strength "I..."

- ◎ Act clearly and confidently when making choices and taking action.

- ◎ Can find my way back to a calm, centered place even during times of stress, doubt or uncertainty.

- ◎ Have a strong, consistent and clear connection with my Inner Wisdom. I know how to communicate and consult my Inner Wisdom when making choices and decisions.

- ◎ Trust my intuition more than my rationale mind and have the strength to follow it even when it stretches me out of my comfort zone or it differs from conventional wisdom.

- ◎ Listen to my opinions and feelings over those of others and follow my truth even if others do or say things differently.

Heart & Soul Sparks

add personal spark to your heart art

Think of something in your life where you are facing uncertainty or doubt, or where you are being stretched outside of your comfort zone, or where your intellect is telling you that your intuition is crazy. Close your eyes, put your hand on your heart, and take a breath (this is how you access your Inner Wisdom), ask your Inner Wisdom the questions below. Listen or feel for an answer (may be a word, an image or a knowing or sensation) and write down your Inner Wisdom's response. If nothing comes (if you haven't been talking lately that can happen), imagine you were giving a friend you loved wise counsel. What would you say to her?

- 💗 What does my Inner Wisdom know about <insert situation>?

- 💗 What wise actions can I take to step forward?

- 💗 What is the loving truth I need to hear to have the courage to step forward and trust my inner wisdom?

Write these wise words into your Heart Art to super power your ability to trust and follow your truth.

Self-Worth

Believing and making all choices from the truth that you are enough, just as you are, right now. Choosing to value yourself and your success from the inside out, not based on external validation or standards.

12/31/17

What messes up self-worth: 1) comparison 2) judging myself by unrealistic expectations - advertising, society, family - any outside system 3) future tripping - could, should - not being present 4) looking for validation, recognition or adoration from outside 5) overgiving, overdoing and overworking to prove my value - value giving over receiving.

Most damaging is comparison. "Honey, you are enough right now." or "Kaopa, you have done enough." What would enough be? Ask and only do that.

Signs of Strong Self-Worth

On a scale of 1 to 5, with 5 being always true, 3 sometimes true and 1 not true, rank your self-love strength "I..."

- Believe that I am enough.

- Believe that I am making a difference and that the difference I am making is enough.

- Believe that my presence is enough.

- Know what success and prosperity are for me on all levels – spiritual, material, emotional and relational – and live my life according to these inner guideposts regardless of what others say success is.

- Value who I am and what I do and give as important and significant – no comparison, just an inner knowing that who I am and what I give is valuable.

Heart & Soul Sparks

add personal spark to your heart art

When you value yourself, you can offer your gifts and your presence in your work and relationships fully and freely. Often we just can't see the progress or impact we have made, so we get caught in the comparison trap and de-value just how successful and impactful we are. Use these inquiries to boost your self-worth:

- Name three people whose lives you have made a difference in. How are their lives different because of your presence?

- Name three successes you've had in the past three years – things you have done. What does this tell you about your presence?

- Name three ways you have grown and changed over the past several years that required you to trust and value your unique path. What does this tell you about your presence?

- Name 10 things you love about yourself - things you value, like, or adore.

What do these say about who YOU ARE in your core? These are reflections of the value of your presence. Put some of your presence and the impact it's had into your Heart Art to reflect your innate value.

Congratulations Love!

YOU HAVE TAKEN A BOLD AND BEAUTIFUL STEP TOWARDS CULTIVATING MORE LOVE IN THIS WORLD – BY CHOOSING TO GIVE LOVE TO YOURSELF.

Self-love is the foundation of everything in your life. When you have the inner strength to choose the loving action for and towards yourself, everything flows and feels better even during times of stress and stretch – from your relationships, to your career, to your health and wealth, to your overall personal wellness and happiness.

As I mentioned in the beginning of our journey, self-love is like medicine for your body, heart, mind, and soul. By exploring the inquiries, coloring the images and adding your own personal flair to them, you have created a stronger foundation of courage, compassion, care, and confidence inside yourself.

You don't have to stop there! Keep using the Heart Art for those moments when you need a love, courage, or confidence boost, a big shot of compassion or inner wisdom truth, or a permission slip to express yourself or take care of and stay true to yourself, even if that means disappointing another.

Self-love is a choice, a practice and a path. I invite you to continue this practice and path for your entire life. The more you choose love for yourself, the more you can be that love for who and what matters most to you in this world.

This world needs your beautiful, strong, one-of-a-kind heart.

Who you are matters.
What you need matters.
What you desire matters.

Remember that you are sacred...
and that your presence is enough.

Now let's go into the world and beam that love from the inside out – knowing that a woman who chooses to love, including herself, is powerful, beautiful, and free.

With great heart,

Christine Arylo ♡

Christine Arylo
Founder of The Path of Self-Love School

Want to Super Power Your Self-Love?

Four steps you can take to explore, deepen, and strengthen your inner self-love foundation

 ## One: Take the FREE Self-Love Pulse Check

Determine where your self-love foundation is strong and where it is weak

I created this "Self-Love Pulse Check" as a way for you to check in on the strength of your self-love foundation. Based on the five Gates and Promises of Self-Love, you will receive a full Self-Love Pulse Check Report that reveals your scoring for all five Gates of Self-Love – the five foundations for a deep, unwavering, and strong self-love and inner foundation. You will be able to see where your foundation is weak and where it is strong so you can focus your inner work on where it will have the most impact.

Go to www.SelfLoveQuiz.com

 ## Two: Read a Best-Selling Self-Love Book

Take a self-led journey to strengthen your self-love

I have written three best-selling self-love books that you can dive into and take a self-led journey to strengthen your self-love in these specific ways:

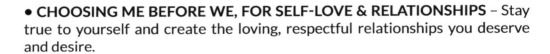 • **CHOOSING ME BEFORE WE, FOR SELF-LOVE & RELATIONSHIPS** – Stay true to yourself and create the loving, respectful relationships you deserve and desire.

 • **MADLY IN LOVE WITH ME, THE SELF-LOVE GO-TO GUIDEBOOK** – Strengthen all 10 branches of self-love. Create a strong self-love foundation that supports all areas of your life.

 • **REFORM YOUR INNER MEAN GIRL, 7 STEPS TO TRANSFORMING SELF-BULLYING INTO SELF-LOVE** – Reveal what kind of Inner Critic you have (there are 13 types specific to women). Learn to transform your inner sabotaging force and start making more self-supporting, self-empowering choices.

To learn more, go to
www.TheSelfLoveBooks.com

Available at Amazon, Barnes & Noble, IndieBound, & Book Depository
(International orders) – in English, Audiobooks, and Other Languages

Three: Take a Self-Love Foundations Class, Intensive, or Immersion at The Path of Self-Love School

Self-love is not something most people know 'how' to do. Even though it is our natural state to choose love, we are imprinted from a very early age with all kinds of self-sabotaging thoughts, habits and beliefs that keep us from the true desires of our hearts and souls, make us incredibly hard on ourselves, and cause us to sacrifice and settle.

Reading a book is a great way to strengthen your self-love. You can gain information and insight. And... to make shift that sticks, we need transformational structures that can support us to make changes in our lives. This is why I founded The Path of Self-Love™ School, an international school that has served over 35,000 students from the ages of 8 to 88. We offer the teachings + the structure + the support + the community for those who desire to create a strong inner foundation based on self-compassion, confidence, empowerment, trust, care, acceptance, esteem, and expression, including:

• **SELF-LOVE FOUNDATIONS, MONTHLY CLASSES TO STRENGTHEN THE 10 BRANCHES OF SELF-LOVE** – We call it The Love Club, and month-by-month you strengthen each branch of self-love through a daily practice, in-depth teaching, meditation, daring acts of love, and more.

• **SELF-LOVE INTENSIVES, 40-DAY BREAKTHROUGH PROGRAMS** – Choose a specific area of self-love you desire a breakthrough in, and you can break self-sabotaging patterns and imprint new self-loving habits. Each practice focuses on one of the five foundational gates of self-love.

• **SELF-LOVE IMMERSIONS, IN-PERSON RETREATS** – To make shift happen, stepping out of your life and spending time in a sacred, intentional space with others can be one of the most powerful and supportive experiences. It's like self-love dynamite!

To learn more, go to
www.SelfLovePrograms.com

 ## Four: Work with a Certified Self-Love Guide

Personally trained and mentored by Christine Arylo, our guides are masters at creating customized transformational paths for a specific amount of time. You will use these paths to put the practices, wisdom, and tools to use in your day-to-day life, with support, guidance, and accountability to assist you in making different choices rooted in self-love.

To learn more go to
www.FindASelfLoveCoach.com

Want to Share the Love?

We are on a mission to serve 1 billion people the medicine of self-love.
To make the self-love teachings accessible to all.
And within three generations to create a world where every child born
is born connected to love and stays connected to that love
because they know how to source love from within.

We are gathering & organizing... join us!

Join the Path of Self-Love Teacher Training

A Premier Training for Those Who Desire to Make a Bigger Difference by More Masterfully and Powerfully Teaching and Guiding Others Using the Power of Self-Love

The Path of Self-Love Training gives you access and mastery to some of the best self-love "technology" in the world – techniques, tools, processes, and skills – that are tested and proven, so you can more masterfully and powerfully guide, coach, assess, teach, and prescribe self-love to individuals or groups in practical, tangible, potent, and fun ways that empower people to make self-loving choices in every area of their lives.

We are currently training people of many backgrounds, serving many different communities, on six continents. Some are teaching others already, others desire to guide others at some point, and all are using this potent self-love medicine with themselves and in their families and communities. We need a rainbow of people to get this self-love medicine to the people. We'd love to connect with you!

To learn more, go to
www.SelfLoveTraining.com

Become a Self-Love Ambassador- It's Free!

Lead a circle or event in your community on International Self-Love Day, February 13th

Be part of a global community of people who believe in the power of love and are daring enough to share the message of self-love with the world. Every February 13th, in honor of International Self-Love Day, ambassadors from all over the world hold self-love focused circles and events. As an ambassador, you receive:

• The Self-Love Circle Guide, with all the details you need to create a powerful and fun event

• An Art of Sacred Circle Training Workshop Session with Christine Arylo

• Access to the Self-Love Ambassador online community

Learn more and join us – it's free!
www.SelfLoveAmbassador.com

79

Share this Self-Love Journal & Coloring Journey with a Girl or Woman You Love

One of our favorite things is to hear stories about how women and girls received one of our books from their mother, sister, friend, aunt, grandmother, godmother, teacher, or even man in their lives. This coloring journal is designed for girls and for women in a way that makes it easy to give it as a gift of LOVE. It's like saying "Hey, I see you. You matter to me."

Send some love to a woman or girl you love today...
www.SelfLoveColoringBook.com

Follow The Path of Self Love & Receive Love Boosts

 BLOG: www.TheSelfLoveBlog.com

 FACEBOOK: @PathofSelfLove

 TWITTER: @PathofSelfLove

 INSTAGRAM: @PathofSelfLove

Heart Art by Sue Bevins, Self Love Guide

Thank You

FROM MY HEART TO YOURS

TO YOU, BRAVE, COURAGEOUS SOUL... thank you for choosing to believe in the power of self-love by doing whatever part of this self-love coloring journal you chose. Whether you bought this journal for yourself or received it as a gift, choosing to heal, free, and strengthen your inner courage, confidence, compassion, and ability to express and stay true to yourself not only makes a huge difference in your life, but it will also affect every person you care about in this world.

TO THOSE WHO HAVE HELPED BIRTH THE PATH OF SELF-LOVE SCHOOL AND THE INTERNATIONAL SELF-LOVE MOVEMENT... THANK YOU. Your presence has kept me going all these years when people thought I was crazy to leave my corporate job to found a self-love school. For over a decade, we have stood for self-love when #selflove was anything but loving. It has been you showing up as Love Ambassadors, students and sisters and fellow teachers, that has kept me going in my times of doubt and personal stretch. This is why I say self-love is a choice, practice, and path... I myself still use these tools and practices every day.

TO ALL OF YOU WITH DREAMS... this book of Heart Art has been a dream of mine to rediscover and reclaim the artist I left behind at the age of 19, when I compared myself to others and thought my art was not good enough to offer to the world (even though I had been drawing since I could hold a Crayola marker). It's a testament to the self-empowerment that I lacked a year into college, when adults said I had to be "more practical" in my career choices, and I set down my pastels and markers for a marketing degree. I did not know then what I know now, which is I did not have to choose between the two. I did not need to abandon any part of me. Together, expressed, I can be both an MBA and an artist. Both make me who I am. The same is true for you too. All parts of you are needed to be fully and freely expressed.

TO THOSE WHO ENCOURAGED AND SUPPORTED ME TO BRING THIS DREAM INTO REALITY... including my dear soul sister Shiloh Sophia McCloud, founder of the Intentional Creativity Foundation, and her mentor Sue Hoya Sellars, for helping me re-find my artist and find this feminine heart image which wanted so to be born – and all came together in our very special trip to Paris. To Sharon Zeugin, master calligrapher and teacher, thank you for helping me "find my font" and giving me permission to let my style be more than enough.

To Noah, my soul partner, who has stood by me on this journey to make self-love a reality for over a decade, always believing in the vision and giving so much of himself to support me and the women and girls we serve. To Shannon Kaiser, whose design skills and big heart helped me bring this into form, thank you for all the years of working together. To the Path of Self-Love teachers and guides, including Stacey Hoffer and Lea Guthrie, and Sue Bevins who lead our programs, and without whom I would not be able to bring these teachings into the world. And to anyone I forgot but who has been part of this self-love movement – thank you! I love you and I am forever grateful to you.

May love reign and may love grow in its power on this planet,
in large part because we choose and know how to love ourselves.

About Christine Arylo
FOUNDER OF THE PATH OF SELF-LOVE SCHOOL

Christine Arylo is a women's leadership advisor, transformational speaker and teacher, and bestselling author who leads retreats, workshops, and programs around the world, working with women to make shift happen – in the lives they lead and in the work they do. She combines her 15 years of corporate MBA experience in marketing, strategy, and leadership communications with her 15 years of spiritual study of the divine feminine, yogic, and earth-based wisdom traditions to guide women how to live and lead their lives, businesses, and relationships the "feminine way": professionally successful, internally empowered, and personally sustainable and satisfying.

For more than a decade, she has been a catalyst, mentor, and advisor for executives, emerging leaders, and visionary entrepreneurs at organizations such as Gap Inc., Salesforce, Genetech, and Google. Over 35,000 people have participated in and benefited from her personal transformational programs and workshops. She has appeared on CBS, NBC, and FOX; blogs regularly for the Huffington Post and Thrive; and is the host of the Feminine Power Time podcast (www.FemininePowerTime.com).

Learn more about Christine at
www.ChristineArylo.com

Follow Christine for inspiration and feminine wisdom
Feminine Power Time Podcast:
Subscribe on iTunes or Stitcher or go to www.FemininePowerPodcast.com

 FACEBOOK:
@CHRISTINEARYLOSPEAKS

 TWITTER:
@CHRISTINEARYLO

 INSTAGRAM:
@CHRISTINEARYLO

 YOUTUBE:
@CHRISTINEARYLO

There is nothing more powerful, beautiful, or free than a woman who truly loves - including herself.

—Christine Arylo

Made in the USA
San Bernardino, CA
23 June 2017